Answers

C000178421

Biology

Section 1 — Cells and Respiration

Page 9 — Magic Microscope Questions
Quick Fire Questions
Q1   Making objects look bigger.
Q2   To stick an object onto before you look at it under the microscope.

Practice Questions
Q1   (a)

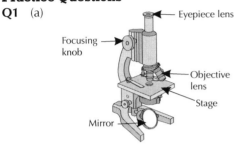

Eyepiece lens
Focusing knob
Objective lens
Stage
Mirror

(b)   The longest lens.
(c)   eyepiece lens
Q2   1 — Adjust the mirror so that light shines up through the hole in the stage.
2 — Clip the slide onto the stage.
3 — Select the lowest-powered objective lens.
4 — Move the objective lens down to just above the slide.
5 — Look down the microscope.
6 — Adjust the focus to get a clear image.

Pages 11-12 — Super Cell Questions
Quick Fire Questions
Q1   cell membrane
Q2   In the mitochondria.
Q3   In the vacuole.

Practice Questions
Q1

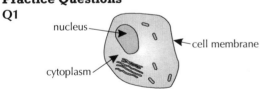

nucleus
cell membrane
cytoplasm

Q2   (a)

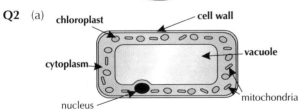

chloroplast
cell wall
cytoplasm
vacuole
nucleus
mitochondria

(b)   Any two from: e.g. cell wall / vacuole / chloroplasts
Q3   A — 3 (The nucleus controls what the cell does.)
B — 2 (Chloroplasts are where photosynthesis happens.)
C — 4 (The cytoplasm is where most chemical reactions in the cell happen.)
D — 1 (The cell membrane controls what goes in and out of the cell.)
Q4   (a)   unicellular
(b)   E.g. to help it swim.

Pages 14-15 —
Organisation (
Quick Fire Ques
Q1   A group of organs that work together.
Q2   A substance moves from where there's lots of it to where there's less of it.
Q3   true

Practice Questions
Q1   1 — cell, **2 — tissue**, 3 — **organ**, **4 — organ system**, 5 — **organism**
Q2   an organ
Remember, an organ is a group of different tissues working together.
Q3   Cell organisation happens in **multicellular** organisms.
Q4   Diffusion is needed to move things into and out of a cell.
Q5   (a)   e.g. leaf
(b)   e.g. stomach
Q6   (a)   a tissue
Remember, a tissue is a group of similar cells working together.
(b)   inside, membrane, diffusion

Pages 17-18 — Refreshing Respiration Questions
Quick Fire Questions
Q1   true
Q2   energy

Practice Questions
Q1   mitochondria
Q2   It releases the energy organisms need to stay alive.
Q3   **glucose** + oxygen → **carbon dioxide** + **water** + ENERGY
When you're writing a word equation, it doesn't matter what order you write the reactants and the products in — as long as the reactants come before the arrow and the products come after.
Q4   more, anaerobic, lactic acid
Q5   (a)(i) glucose → carbon dioxide + ethanol + ENERGY
(ii) fermentation
(b)   carbon dioxide
(c)(i) The temperature of the water bath.
The independent variable is the thing you change in an experiment.
(ii) e.g. accurate

Section 2 — Humans as Organisms

Pages 20-21 — Nutty Nutrition Questions
Quick Fire Questions
Q1   energy
Q2   Any two from, e.g. butter, cooking oil, cream.
Q3   true

Practice Questions
Q1   (a)   It helps to move food through the digestive system.
(b)   e.g. constipation
(c)   Breakfast cereal, peas, carrots, oats and bananas should be underlined.

Answers

Q2 E.g. because all the chemical reactions in your body happen in water.

Q3 (a) True
(b) True
(c) False
(d) True
(e) False

Q4 (a)(i) Any two from: e.g. fruits, vegetables, cereals.
(ii) It helps wounds/cuts to heal.
(b) **Calcium** is needed for strong bones and teeth.
Iron is needed for healthy blood.

Q5 (a) fish
(b) To help us grow and repair damage.

Page 24 — Mega More on Nutrition Questions

Quick Fire Questions

Q1 E.g. it can cause slow growth in children. / It can cause irregular periods in women.

Q2 E.g. scurvy — causes problems with the skin and gums.

Practice Questions

Q1 more, obesity, food, minerals, deficiency diseases

Q2 (a) Eve
Eve is heavier, so she will need more energy.
(b) Daily BER (kJ/day) = 5.4 × 24 × 70 = **9072** kJ/day
(c) Energy need for swimming = 1800 ÷ 2
= **900** kJ
You need to divide by two here because Eve swims for half an hour (so she needs half the amount of energy needed for one hour's swimming).
(d) Energy needed in total = 900 + BER
= 900 + 9072
= **9972** kJ/day

Pages 26-27 — Daring Digestion Questions

Quick Fire Questions

Q1 the mouth

Q2 e.g. liver and pancreas

Q3 Any two from: pancreas, small intestine, stomach, mouth.

Practice Questions

Q1 1 — mouth
2 — gullet
3 — stomach
4 — small intestine
5 — large intestine

Q2 (a) False
(b) True
(c) True
(d) False
(e) False

Q3 The pancreas contains **glandular** tissue.
This tissue makes **enzymes** to break down **food**.

Q4 (a) bile
(b) It breaks fats into tiny droplets.

Q5 (a) mechanical and chemical
(b) It moves the stomach wall to churn up food.
(c)(i) proteins, carbohydrates
(ii) E.g. they speed up the rate of chemical reactions in the body. / They are biological catalysts.

Pages 29-30 — Mighty More on Digestion Questions

Quick Fire Questions

Q1 in the blood

Q2 villi

Practice Questions

Q1 Small molecules are absorbed into the blood.

Q2 Thin outer layer of cells — The molecules don't need to travel far to get into the blood.
Large surface area — Lots of food molecules can be absorbed at the same time.

Q3 Any two from: e.g. they make enzymes, they make useful vitamins, they stop harmful bacteria growing.

Q4 (a) enzymes
(b) A food high in glucose. The glucose can pass straight into the bloodstream and raise the blood glucose level. If you eat a food high in starch, the starch needs to be broken down into glucose first before it can pass into the bloodstream, so it will take longer for the blood glucose level to be raised.

Pages 32-33 — Splendid Skeleton and Muscles Questions

Quick Fire Questions

Q1 The skull.

Q2 true

Q3 A tough band that attaches a muscle to a bone.

Practice Questions

Q1 movement

Q2 Humerus — arm
Breast bone — chest
Jaw — head
Femur — leg

Q3 tendon, contracts, move

Q4 (a) They are pairs of muscles that work **against each other**.
(b)

	To make the arm bend:	To make the arm straighten:
Which muscle contracts?	biceps	triceps
Which muscle relaxes?	triceps	biceps

Q5 (a)(i) tough, organs, lungs
(ii) To make red blood cells and white blood cells.
(b) It acts as a rigid frame for the rest of the body to hang off.

Pages 35-36 — Graceful Gas Exchange Questions

Quick Fire Questions

Q1 oxygen and carbon dioxide

Q2 the ribcage

Q3 In the alveoli.

Practice Questions

Q1 1 — Trachea, **2 — Bronchus,**
3 — Bronchioles, 4 — Alveoli

Q2 It helps to get air in and out of the lungs.

Answers

Q3

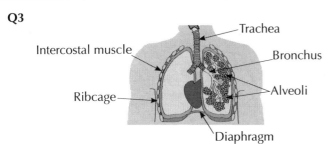

Trachea
Intercostal muscle
Bronchus
Ribcage
Alveoli
Diaphragm

Q4 (a)(i) B
(ii) A
(b) Because oxygen is needed for respiration and the body needs to get rid of carbon dioxide.
Q5 E.g. they're moist. They've got a good blood supply. They've got a large surface area.

Pages 38-39 — Brilliant Breathing Questions

Quick Fire Questions
Q1 When you breathe in.
Q2 Measuring lung volume.

Practice Questions
Q1 (a)(i) the balloons
(ii) the rubber sheet
(b) trachea
(c)(i) They inflate / fill with air.
(ii) increases, decreases, in, inflates
Q2 (a) it decreases
(b) They inflate / fill with air.
(c) it increases

Pages 41-42 — Exotic Exercise, Asthma and Smoking Questions

Quick Fire Questions
Q1 To get more oxygen to your muscles (for respiration).
Q2 false

Practice Questions
Q1 (a) e.g. pet hairs / smoke
(b) the bronchioles
(c) Dust can cause Darren to have an asthma attack. An asthma attack will make it difficult for Darren to breathe. Dust could make the lining of Darren's airways become swollen.
(d) They will contract.
Q2 (a) E.g. it gets faster and deeper.
(b) oxygen, respire, energy
(c) She may have developed more small blood vessels in her lungs.
(d) It allows her to get more air into her lungs when she breathes in.
Q3 (a)(i) cilia
(ii) They move mucus out of your airways.
(b) The tar in cigarette smoke damages the cilia/little hairs in the airways. This causes mucus to stick in the airways, which makes the smoker cough more.

Pages 44-45 — Handy Human Reproduction Questions

Quick Fire Questions
Q1 sperm
Q2 the ovaries

Practice Questions
Q1 (a) C
(b) the sperm duct
(c)(i) E
(ii) A testis.
(d) Sperm leaves the penis through structure D (the urethra) during sexual intercourse.
Q2

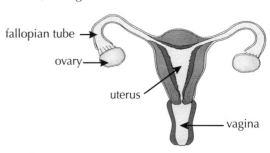

fallopian tube
ovary
uterus
vagina

Q3 (a) The fallopian tube.
(b) uterus
(c) It breaks down and passes out of the vagina (during a period).
Q4 (a) The nucleus of a sperm cell and the nucleus of an egg cell combine.
(b) an embryo

Page 47 — Merry Menstrual Cycle Questions

Quick Fire Questions
Q1 28 days
Q2 It is maintained.

Practice Questions
Q1 (a) The monthly reproductive cycle in a female.
(b)(i) day 14
(ii) day 4
(iii) day 1
Q2 (a) To make it ready for a fertilised egg to land there.
(b)(i) stage one
(ii) It passes out of the vagina.
(iii) 3 to 4 days

Page 49 — Helpful Having a Baby Questions

Quick Fire Questions
Q1 It is the time between the egg being fertilised and the baby being born.
Q2 The uterus lining.
Q3 true

Practice Questions
Q1 (a) foetus
(b) 39, 7
(c) E.g. it might be quite small. It might have problems breathing.

Answers

Q2 (a) e.g.

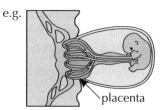

placenta

(b) E.g. it lets the foetus get oxygen/food from the mother's blood.

Pages 51-52 — Dangerous (Health and) Drugs Questions

Quick Fire Questions
Q1 A drug used for enjoyment, rather than as medicine.
Q2 Sensitivity and movement.
Q3 E.g. brain / liver.

Practice Questions
Q1 Drugs can affect life processes.
Drugs can damage your health.
Alcohol is a drug.
Q2 (a) body, mind/brain
(b) Anything that affects the way the body works.
(c)(i) e.g. heroin and LSD
(ii) E.g. it can lead to dehydration/death.
(d) It means the user feels like they need to have the drug.
Q3 (a) e.g. paint / glue
(b) E.g. they can make you see and hear things that are not really there.
(c) Any two from: e.g. lungs / brain / kidneys.
Q4 (a)(i) Before drinking the alcohol.
(ii) decreases, slowly
(b) E.g. sensitivity, because it makes you take longer to respond/react. / Movement, because you move more slowly.
(c) He could repeat the investigation at least three times. If the results are the same/very similar, they are repeatable.

Section 3 — Plants and Ecosystems

Pages 54-55 — Pesky Plant Nutrition Questions

Quick Fire Questions
Q1 glucose
Q2 chloroplasts
Q3 They are tiny holes on the bottom of the leaf. They let carbon dioxide into the leaf and oxygen out.

Practice Questions
Q1 water, minerals
Q2 **water** + carbon dioxide $\xrightarrow{\text{sunlight}}$ **glucose + oxygen**
It doesn't matter which way round you put glucose and oxygen — as long as they both come after the arrow.
Q3 broad, large, light, chloroplasts, light
Q4 (a) James' plant has been in the light, so it has been able to photosynthesise and make food (glucose), which is used to grow. Jessica's plant has been in the dark, so it hasn't been able to photosynthesise and produce food, so it has died.

(b) Over several weeks, plants that are kept on a windowsill will (e.g.) **grow bigger but plants grown in a cupboard will die.**

Pages 57-58 — Radical (Plant) Reproduction Questions

Quick Fire Questions
Q1 male
Q2 to get food

Practice Questions
Q1 female, ovary, male, anther
Q2 (a)

Name of Flower Part	Letter on Diagram	Male or Female?
Anther	B	Male
Ovary	E	**Female**
Filament	**A**	Male
Style	D	Female
Stigma	**C**	**Female**

(b) C, D and E
Q3 (a) By the wind.
(b)(i) They attract insects.
(ii) E.g a sticky stigma.
Q4 Insects visit rose flowers to get food. When they visit a flower, pollen sticks to them. When the insects visit another flower, this pollen is pulled off them by the flower's sticky stigma. This pollinates the second flower.

Pages 61-62 — Fun Fertilisation and Seed Formation Questions

Quick Fire Questions
Q1 the embryo
Q2 the ovary
Q3 explosions
Q4 E.g. horse chestnut trees.

Practice Questions
Q1 (a) C
(b)

Your X should be over the ovule.

(c) The nucleus of a male sex cell and the nucleus of a female sex cell come together.
Q2 A plant that has fruit, which are covered in tiny hooks. — animals
A plant with very light seeds surrounded by feathery strands. — wind
A plant that has seeds in pods, which dry out in the Sun. — explosions
A plant that has very heavy fruit. — drop and roll
Q3 seed, ovules, seed dispersal

Answers

Q4 1 — A pollen grain lands on a stigma.
2 — A pollen tube grows down to the ovary.
3 — A nucleus from a male sex cell travels from the pollen grain to the ovary.
4 — The nucleus from a male sex cell joins with the nucleus of a female sex cell.

Q5 (a) By the wind.
(b) Dandelion fruits have a parachute. This helps them to catch the wind and be blown away.
(c) e.g. sycamore

Pages 64-65 — Interesting Investigating Seed Dispersal Questions

Quick Fire Questions
Q1 (at least) three
Q2 To make sure it is a fair test.

Practice Questions
Q1 (a) 1. The independent variable in this experiment is **the type of fruit Amanda drops**.
2. The dependent variable in this experiment is **the distance the seeds travel**.
Remember, the independent variable is the thing you change in an experiment. The dependent variable is the effect you measure.
(b) Any two of: e.g. the height the fruit is dropped from / the speed of the fan / the person dropping the fruit / the place she's doing the experiment.
(c)

Trial Number	Distance Travelled (cm)	
	Seed A	Seed B
1	11	135
2	12	122
3	13	127
Mean	(11 + 12 + 13) ÷ 3 = **12**	(135 + 122 + 127) ÷ 3 = **128**

(d) Seed A
(e)

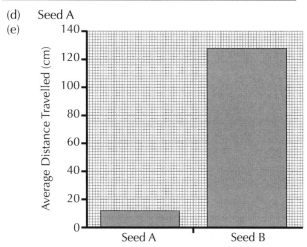

Make sure you label the axes clearly, and remember to put in the units.
(f) Seed B because it travelled much further than seed A in the experiment.

You would expect the wind-dispersed seed to travel the furthest in this experiment because the fan acts like the wind would.

Pages 67-68 — Delightful Dependence Questions

Quick Fire Questions
Q1 e.g. light energy
Q2 In molecules (like proteins) in their cells.
Q3 They pollinate crops.

Practice Questions
Q1 The organisms in an ecosystem need each other to survive.
Q2 All the living things in one area, plus **their environment**.
Q3 gases, oxygen, respiration, high
Q4 (a) the Sun
(b) Any two of: e.g. the gases in the air / the amount of light / the temperature.
(c) pollination/reproduction
(d)(i) e.g.

One arrow should point from the Sun to the grass. The other arrow should point from the grass to the mouse.
(ii) The mouse can't get energy directly from the Sun / carry out photosynthesis. So it needs the grass to capture the Sun's energy.

Pages 70-72 — Formal Food Chain and Food Web Questions

Quick Fire Questions
Q1 Many food chains joined together.
Q2 a producer / a plant
Q3 An animal that eats producers/plants.

Practice Questions
Q1 The arrows in a food chain show the direction of energy flow.
Q2 (a) Any two from:
Oak tree ➝ aphids ➝ ladybird ➝ blackbird ➝ hawk
Oak tree ➝ caterpillar ➝ blackbird ➝ hawk
Oak tree ➝ caterpillar ➝ thrush ➝ hawk
Oak tree ➝ beetle ➝ blackbird ➝ hawk
Oak tree ➝ beetle ➝ thrush ➝ hawk
Oak tree ➝ snail ➝ thrush ➝ hawk
(b)(i) The aphids, caterpillar, beetle and snail should be circled.
Anything that eats the oak tree (the producer) is a primary consumer.
(ii) thrush/blackbird/ladybird
Remember, a secondary consumer eats primary consumers.

Answers

(c) If the number of aphids decreases — the number of ladybirds might decrease.
If the number of beetles increases — the number of blackbirds might increase.
If the number of hawks increases — the number of thrushes might decrease.

Q3 (a) the pond weed
(b) fish
(c)(i) It might reduce the number of frogs.
(ii) It might increase the number of worms.

Q4 (a) the kestrel
(b) The number of kestrels will decrease. This is because each kestrel will have a high level of poison in its body, so kestrels will lay eggs with thin shells. This makes it less likely that chicks will survive.

Section 4 — Inheritance, Variation and Survival

Pages 74-75 — Dopey DNA Questions

Quick Fire Questions
Q1 True
Q2 The nucleus.
Q3 They were the first scientists to build a model of DNA.

Practice Questions
Q1 A gene is a short length of DNA.
Q2 (a) DNA
(b) a hereditary characteristic
(c) a chromosome
(d) the nucleus
Q3 chromosomes, characteristics
Q4 (a) They produced data that was used by Crick and Watson to build a model of DNA.
(b) It is a spiral made from two chains twisted together.
Q5 (a) Because they have genes from both of their parents and genes control characteristics.
(b) heredity
Q6 Yes. The condition is controlled by her genes and she got her genes from her parents.
Remember, hereditary characteristics are ones that you get from your parents through your genes.

Page 77 — Vital Variation Questions

Quick Fire Questions
Q1 e.g. height / weight
Q2 e.g. blood group / the colour of a courgette

Practice Questions
Q1 Two members of different species.
Q2 A difference between members of the same species.
Q3 Continuous variation, because e.g. the amount of milk produced can take any value in a range / the bars on the graph touch.

Pages 79-80 — Stunning Natural Selection and Survival Questions

Quick Fire Questions
Q1 Any two of: e.g. light / water / minerals from the soil
Q2 Any two of: e.g. food / water / shelter

Practice Questions
Q1 compete, not enough, survive, better
Q2 Derek
Q3 (a) 1 — Birds with bigger beaks are more likely to survive and reproduce.
2 — The genes for bigger beaks become more common than the genes for smaller beaks.
3 — All the birds on the island eventually have bigger beaks.
(b) natural selection
Q4 Group A, because these are the most likely to hear a fox coming and be able to run away from it. This means they are more likely to survive and reproduce, so pass on the genes for their useful characteristics to their offspring. Over time, their useful characteristics are likely to become more common than those of the other hares.

Pages 82-83 — Exciting Extinction and Preserving Species Questions

Quick Fire Questions
Q1 False
A species is extinct when there are none of them left at all.
Q2 An endangered species.

Practice Questions
Q1 The variety of species living on the Earth.
Q2 Changing the environment of all the species on Earth will help to protect them.
If a species becomes extinct it will not affect any other species.
Q3 environment, compete, decrease
Q4 (a) A collection of seeds / a gene bank (for plants).
(b) If a plant species has its seeds stored in a seed bank, then if it becomes extinct we could grow new plants from the seeds.

Chemistry

Section 1 — Classifying Materials

Page 8 — Saucy Solid, Liquid and Gas Questions

Quick Fire Questions
Q1 solid, liquid and gas
Q2 liquids and gases

Practice Questions
Q1 (a) solid
(b) liquid
(c) gas
(d) solid
(e) solid
(f) gas

Answers

Q2

Property	State of Matter
Easily squashed	Gas
Definite shape	Solid
No definite volume	Gas
Does not flow	Solid
High density	Solid
Medium density	Liquid

Pages 10-11 — Positive Particle Theory Questions

Quick Fire Questions
Q1 They are held close together by strong forces.
Q2 The particles are free to move past each other.
Q3 There is a lot of space between the particles.
Q4 gas

Practice Questions
Q1

solid   liquid   gas

Q2 The true statements are:
Solid particles are held very close together.
Weak forces hold the particles together in liquids.
The particles in liquids are free to move past each other.
Gases spread out to fill their container.

Q3 You **can't** push in the plungers in the sand and water syringes. This is because the particles in the sand and water are very **close together**.
The particles in the air syringe are **far apart** to start with. When you push in the plunger, the air particles get **closer together**.

Q4 (a) It has no fixed shape.
(b) E.g. they have no regular arrangement/pattern. / They are able to move. / There's a weaker attraction between particles.

Pages 14-15 — Magical More Particle Theory Questions

Quick Fire Questions
Q1 melting
Q2 They gain more energy and vibrate more.
Q3 Particles spreading out.

Practice Questions
Q1 (a)

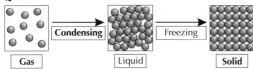

(b) As substance X cools, its particles move **more slowly**. This is because they have **less** energy.
(c)(i) It increases.
(ii) The particles are held more closely together.

Q2 (a) E.g.

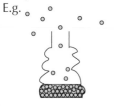

(b) E.g. the perfume particles diffuse/move from where there are lots of them (the bottle) to where there are less of them (the air outside the bottle).

Q3 (a) The dye particles spread out from where there are lots of them to where there are fewer of them. It takes a few hours for the black particles to be spread out evenly in the water.
(b) diffusion

Pages 18-19 — Ace Atoms and Elements Questions

Quick Fire Questions
Q1 The smallest, simplest type of particle.
Q2 one or two
Q3 groups

Practice Questions
Q1 (a) The following statements should be ticked:
All matter is made up of atoms.
There are different types of atom.
(b) E.g. each element contains only one type of atom. Elements can be solids, liquids or gases.

Q2 O — oxygen, C — carbon, Fe — iron, Br — bromine, Al — aluminium, H — hydrogen

Q3 (a)(i) Any three of: H, He, C, N, O, Cl, Ar
(ii) Any three of: Li, Mg, K, Mn, Fe, Cu, Zn, Ag, In, Au, Hg
(b) 5
H and He are in period 1 — start counting down from there to work out the numbers of the other periods.
(c) 3
Ignore the big block of metals in the middle of the table when you're counting the groups.

Q4 (a) 1 — lithium, Li
2 — sodium, Na
3 — potassium, K
(b) Both metals will react more violently than lithium. This is because the Group 1 metals get more reactive as you go down the group.

Pages 21-22 — Cute Compounds Questions

Quick Fire Questions
Q1 Two or more atoms that are joined/bonded together.
Q2 CO_2, three

Practice Questions
Q1 (a) Water is a compound. It forms when two **hydrogen** atoms combine with one **oxygen** atom. The atoms are joined by **bonds**.
(b) Water has more than one type of atom. Elements only have one type of atom.
(c) The atoms in water are chemically joined. Water contains more than one element.

Q2 (a) **one** sodium atom, **one** chlorine atom
(b) **one** hydrogen atom, **one** fluorine atom
(c) **one** zinc atom, **two** chlorine atoms
(d) **two** hydrogen atoms, **two** oxygen atoms
(e) **two** iron atoms, **three** oxygen atoms
(f) **one** aluminium atom, **three** chlorine atoms

Q3 (a) a compound

(b) Sodium and chlorine react to produce the solid and chemical reactions produce compounds. The properties of the are totally different to those of sodium or chlorine (e.g. the solid can be eaten, but chlorine is poisonous).

Page 24 — Magnificent Mixtures Questions
Quick Fire Questions
Q1 A substance that is made up of only one type of element or only one type of compound. E.g. pure water.
Q2 No
Q3 The substance will dissolve.
Q4 The substance will not dissolve.

Practice Questions
Q1 (a) pure
(b) pure
(c) mixture
Q2 (a) 100 + 10 = **110 g**
(b) solvent
(c) solute
(d) When the salt is added to the water the **bonds** holding the salt particles together break. The salt particles then **mix with** the water molecules to make a solution. The salt **hasn't** disappeared.

Pages 27-29 — Stunning Separating Mixtures Questions
Quick Fire Questions
Q1 a funnel
Q2 Pure water boils at 100 °C. Pure ice melts at 0 °C.

Practice Questions
Q1 (1 — The mixture is heated in a flask.)
2 — The liquid evaporates off as a gas.
3 — The gas is cooled and turns back into a liquid in the condenser.
4 — The liquid is collected in a flask. The solid is left behind.
Q2 (a) To evaporate off the water.
(b) To condense the water vapour into liquid water.
(c) The blue dyes have been left behind in the conical flask.
Q3 (a) chromatography
(b)(i) D
(ii) The spots on the filter paper are in the same place.
Q4 (a) Weigh it on a balance.
(b) Add it to water and stir.
(c) Filter it through filter paper (in a funnel).
(d) Boil it / evaporate off the water.
(e) Percentage = (mass of salt ÷ mass of rock salt) x 100
= (3 ÷ 10) x 100
= **30%**
(f) E.g. repeat the experiment three times and work out an average percentage.

Page 32-33 — Puzzling Properties of Metals Questions
Quick Fire Questions
Q1 smooth/shiny
Q2 They are sonorous.
Q3 It can be drawn into wires.

Practice Questions
Q1 Iron, cobalt and nickel should be circled.
Q2 All metals are **good** conductors of heat and electricity. They allow **electrical** current and **heat** energy to pass through them **easily**.
Q3 (a) B, C, F
(b) A Metals are dense.
D Metals are not brittle. / Metals are ductile.
E Metals can be hammered into shape.
Q4

Metal	Property	A use
Copper	Electrical conductor	**Wires**
Silver	**Shiny**	Jewellery
Aluminium	Malleable	**Car bodies**
Iron	**Strong**	Bridges
Brass	Sonorous	**Gongs**

Pages 36-37 — Perfect Properties of Non-metals Questions
Quick Fire Questions
Q1 false
There are more metal elements than non-metal elements.
Q2 Low, because the forces that hold their particles together are very weak.

Practice Questions
Q1 Non-metals **don't** let heat travel through them easily. That's why **saucepan handles** are made out of non-metals. Non-metals are good **insulators**.
Q2 (a) Xe, Br, O, Cl, C, I, Ne, S, F
(b)(i) xenon (Xe) / oxygen (O) / chlorine (Cl) / neon (Ne) / fluorine (F)
(ii) iodine (I) / sulfur (S) / carbon (C)
Q3 (a) A, C
(b) B Non-metals fill less than half of the Periodic Table.
D Some non-metals float in air.
E Non-metals are usually dull.

Pages 39-40 — Prickly Properties of Other Materials Questions
Quick Fire Questions
Q1 plastics
Q2 E.g. nylon / polythene / PVC
Q3 E.g. porcelain / glass / bone china

Practice Questions
Q1 (a) They are insulators of heat. They can be easily moulded. They are flexible.
(b) They are insulators of heat.
Q2 (a) Concrete
(b) It's made from a mixture of two or more different materials stuck together.

(c) E.g. because the floors of the apartment building will be heavy and concrete can support heavy things / concrete is strong enough to support them.

Q3 (a) E.g. because skis need to be light enough to wear. They also need to be strong enough to support the skier's weight.

(b) E.g. because the helmet needs to be light enough to wear, but strong so it won't break in a crash.

Section 2 — Chemical Changes

Pages 42-43 — Eager Equations Questions

Quick Fire Questions
Q1 reactants
Q2 word equations and symbol equations

Practice Questions
Q1 copper + oxygen → copper oxide should be ticked.

Q2 (a) Reactants: copper oxide, hydrochloric acid
Products: copper chloride, water

(b) copper oxide + hydrochloric acid → copper chloride + water

Q3 (a)(i) lead, sulfur
Pb is the symbol for lead. S is the symbol for sulfur.
(ii) one
(b)(i) two
(ii) two
(iii)one

Q4 C + E → A + D + B
It doesn't matter what order the letters are in, as long as C + E are on the left of the arrow and A + D + B are on the right.

Pages 45-46 — Cracking Chemical Reactions Questions

Quick Fire Questions
Q1 true
Q2 No.

Practice Questions
Q1 The true sentences are: A, C, D

Q2 (a) (H)(Cl)

(b) (O)(O)

Q3 Carol mixed 25 g of colourless sulfuric acid with 2 g of black copper oxide powder. This produced **27 g** of blue copper sulfate solution. The total mass of the products (what she made) was **the same as** the mass of the reactants (what she started with).

Q4 (a) A (white) powder is formed. / The surface of the zinc becomes white.
(b)(i) tongs
(ii) Turn it to the yellow flame / turn it off.

Page 48 — Exciting Examples of Chemical Reactions Questions

Quick Fire Questions
Q1 gained
Q2 E.g. combustion/rusting.
Q3 When you heat a substance and it breaks down.

Practice Questions
Q1 (a) methane + **oxygen** → **carbon dioxide** + **water**
(+ energy)
(b) oxidation (reaction)
(c) It gives off energy/heat/light.
Q2 (a) thermal decomposition
(b) CO_2
(c) lead carbonate → lead oxide + carbon dioxide

Pages 50-51 — Cheerful (More on) Chemical Reactions Questions

Quick Fire Questions
Q1 exothermic
Q2 A substance which speeds up a chemical reaction, without being changed or used up in the reaction itself.

Practice Questions
Q1 (a) exothermic
(b) The temperature increased during the reaction.
Q2 (a) exothermic
(b) endothermic
(c) exothermic
Q3 (a) volume of gas
(b) Any two of: e.g. temperature of the hydrogen peroxide (and catalyst) at the start of the reaction / amount of hydrogen peroxide used / amount of catalyst used.
(c)(i) B
(ii) E.g. because the volume of gas increased the fastest / it's the steepest curve / the curve levelled off the fastest / the reaction finished sooner.

Pages 53-54 — Amazing Acids and Alkalis Questions

Quick Fire Questions
Q1 pH 7
Q2 acid
Q3 blue

Practice Questions
Q1

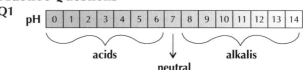

Q2 (a) E.g. lemon juice/citric acid, pH 2
(b) Any two from: e.g. oven cleaner/sodium hydroxide / soap flakes / washing up liquid
(c) E.g. hydrochloric acid/stomach acid
(d) E.g. water
Q3 Universal indicator is a mixture of dyes. It gives lots of different colours. A strong acid makes Universal indicator go **red**. A strong alkali makes it go **purple**. In a neutral solution Universal indicator is **green**.
Q4 (a) red
(b) E.g. Wear safety goggles/gloves when handling the acid.

Answers

Q5

Substance	Colour in red cabbage indicator	Acid or Alkali?
Lemon juice	Red	Acid
Soapy bath water	Turquoise	**Alkali**
Vinegar	Red	**Acid**
Drain cleaner	Yellow	**Alkali**
Washing up liquid	Turquoise	**Alkali**
Lemonade	Red	**Acid**

Pages 56-57 — Neat Neutralisation Reactions Questions

Quick Fire Questions
Q1   an acid and an alkali
Q2   pH 7
Q3   sulfuric acid

Practice Questions
Q1   acid + **alkali** → **salt** + **water**
Q2 (a)(i) hydrochloric acid
      (ii) copper hydroxide
      (iii)copper chloride
    (b)   no
        A different acid will produce a different salt.
Q3 (a)   green
    (b)(i) So he's left with a concentrated solution.
      (ii) To make large crystals of salt.
    (c)(i) sodium chloride
      (ii) water
    (d)(i) Copper sulfate — sulfuric acid
      (ii) Zinc chloride — hydrochloric acid

Pages 59-60 — Rosy Reactivity Series (and Metal Extraction) Questions

Quick Fire Questions
Q1   sodium
Q2   A rock containing metal compounds.
Q3   E.g. potassium / sodium / calcium / magnesium / aluminium

Practice Questions
Q1   Oxygen can be removed from copper oxide to leave copper.
Q2 (a)   1. potassium   2. sodium   3. magnesium
          4. carbon   5. iron   6. gold
    (b)   carbon
Q3 (a)(i) reduction
      (ii) iron oxide + carbon → **iron** + **carbon dioxide**
    (b)   Copper, zinc and lead should be ticked.
    (c)(i) They are above carbon on the reactivity series. / They are more reactive than carbon.
      (ii) electricity

Page 62 — Ready-Made Reactions of Metals (with Acids) Questions

Quick Fire Question
Q1   a salt and hydrogen

Practice Questions
Q1 (a)   E.g. Bubbles of gas appearing. / The zinc granules disappearing/getting smaller.
    (b)   Hold a lit splint to the top of the test tube of gas. If it's hydrogen, it will make a squeaky pop.

Obviously she'll have to take the test tube out of the water first.
    (c)(i) E.g. copper / silver / gold
      (ii) E.g. magnesium

Page 64 — Rocking Reactions of Oxides (with Acids) Questions

Quick Fire Questions
Q1   a metal and oxygen
Q2   true

Practice Questions
Q1 (a)   magnesium oxide
    (b)   neutralisation
    (c)(i) Magnesium sulfate should be circled.
      (ii) water
Q2 (a)   sulfur + oxygen → sulfur dioxide
    (b)   It is **lower** than 7.
    (c)   A salt and water.

Page 66 — Daft Displacement Reactions Questions

Quick Fire Question
Q1   'Taking the place of'

Practice Questions
Q1 (a)   iron + copper sulfate → **iron sulfate** + **copper**
    (b)   A. Magnesium is **more** reactive than zinc.
          B. Copper is **less** reactive than zinc.
          C. Iron is **more** reactive than copper.
          D. Zinc is **more** reactive than iron.
    (c)   1. magnesium   2. zinc   3. iron   4. copper

Section 3 — The Earth and the Atmosphere

Pages 68-69 — Extreme Earth's Surface Questions

Quick Fire Questions
Q1   iron and nickel
Q2   an earthquake

Practice Questions
Q1 (a)   These sentences should be ticked:
         The core is surrounded by the mantle.
         The surface of the Earth is split into many pieces.
         Deep down, the mantle is able to flow very slowly.
    (b)   'The Earth is a solid piece of rock' should be rewritten as, e.g. the Earth is made up of different layers.
         'The crust is the thickest layer of the Earth' should be corrected to, e.g. the crust is the thinnest layer of the Earth.
Q2 (a)   The Earth's **crust** is made of rocks. Quartz is a **mineral** that is found in rocks. Quartz is made up of silicon dioxide, which is a **compound**. Silicon dioxide contains the **elements** silicon and oxygen.
    (b)   an element
Q3 (a)   Any two from: both have a crust. / Both have a mantle. / Both have a core.
    (b)   Mars' core is made of iron and sulfur. Earth's is made of iron and nickel.

Answers

Page 72-73 — Rocking Rock Types Questions

Quick Fire Questions

Q1   magma

Q2   The remains of long dead plants and animals that become trapped in layers of rock.

Q3   sedimentary

Practice Questions

Q1   (a)   igneous

       (b)   Granite and basalt should be underlined.

Q2   (a)   2 — Sediment is laid down at the bottom of lakes and seas. 3 — Layers of sediment build up on top of each other. 4 — Pressure squeezes the water out of the sediments. 5 — The layers eventually become rock.

       (b)   Limestone and sandstone should be underlined.

Q3   (a)   volcano

       (b)   Igneous rocks cool **quickly** above ground. They cool more **slowly** underground. Basalt is an igneous rock with small crystals. It cools **above ground**.

Q4   The layer of rock with the fossil in it will be **older** than the layer above it.
Think about it: the oldest layer will be at the bottom. The youngest layer will be at the top. The layer containing the fossil must have formed before the layers above it.

Q5   (a)   pressure and heat

       (b)   B

       (c)   e.g. marble

Pages 75-76 — Rotten Rock Cycle Questions

Quick Fire Questions

Q1   E.g. by rain / wind / waves.

Q2   They melt.

Practice Questions

Q1   millions of years

Q2   (a)(i) sedimentary rocks

         (ii) heat

       (b)   deposition

       (c)   E.g. wind

       (d)   exposure / It must be revealed on the Earth's surface.

Page 78 — Restful Recycling Questions

Quick Fire Questions

Q1   Something we use that we won't/can't get any more of once it's been used up.

Q2   Taking old, unwanted products and using the materials to make new stuff.

Practice Questions

Q1   E.g. energy, making plastics

Q2   (a)   Recycling aluminium cans is **more** efficient than making brand new aluminium.

       (b)   E.g. they get sent to landfill sites.

       (c)   Any two of: e.g. it uses fewer limited resources, it uses less energy, it's cheaper/saves money, it makes less rubbish.

Page 80 — Charming Carbon Cycle Questions

Quick Fire Questions

Q1   true

Q2   Tiny organisms that break down material.

Practice Questions

Q1   (a)   combustion

       (b)   E.g. through respiration

Q2   (a)   B, D and E should be ticked.

       (b)   A should be rewritten as, e.g. photosynthesis is the process where plants take in carbon dioxide/ make glucose.
C should be rewritten as, e.g. plants take carbon dioxide out of the air by photosynthesis.

Page 82 — All Right Atmosphere and Climate Questions

Quick Fire Questions

Q1   The gases that surround a planet.

Q2   78%

Q3   21%

Practice Questions

Q1   **Carbon dioxide** is one of the gases surrounding the **Earth**. It stops some **heat** from the Sun being lost into **space**.

Q2   (a)   The increase in the Earth's temperature.

       (b)   E.g. burning fossil fuels, chopping down trees/ deforestation

       (c)(i) They might rise.

         (ii) Glaciers and ice sheets covering Greenland and Antarctica are melting faster.

       (d)   Many scientists have collected data about the level of carbon dioxide in the atmosphere. Their results are very similar. This means their data is **reproducible**.

Physics

Section 1 — Energy and Matter

Page 7 — Entertaining Energy Questions

Quick Fire Questions

Q1   Its elastic potential energy store.

Q2   When it's hot.

Q3   E.g. food, fuels, batteries.

Q4   Gravitational potential energy

Practice Questions

Q1   (a)   D

       (b)   E

       (c)   B

Answers

Q2

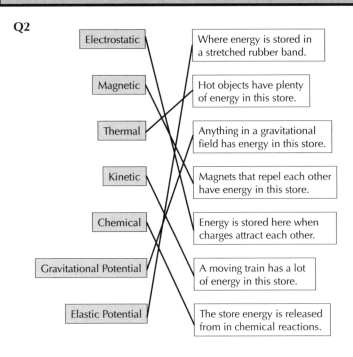

Page 9 — Enchanting Energy Transfer Questions

Quick Fire Questions

Q1 Energy is transferred mechanically from the pen's gravitational potential energy store to its kinetic energy store.

Q2 Energy is transferred electrically from the chemical energy store of the battery to the kinetic energy store of the hands.

Q3 E.g. a car burns petrol to transfer energy from the chemical energy store in the petrol to the car's kinetic energy store.

Practice Questions

Q1 (a) 'Electrically' should be ticked.
(b) 'Chemical to kinetic' should be ticked.

Q2 (a) Gravitational potential → kinetic
(b) Chemical → thermal
(c) Chemical → kinetic
Don't forget that energy can be transferred to more than one energy store.

Pages 11-12 — Even More Exciting Energy Transfer Questions

Quick Fire Questions

Q1 You can use the same amount of energy to apply a **large** force over a small distance or a small force over a **large** distance.

Practice Questions

Q1 (a) chemical
(b) gravitational potential
(c) chemical
(d) elastic

Q2 Alex must supply a **force** to move the pram. This involves a **transfer** of energy. In this case, energy from the **chemical** energy store in the food that Alex has eaten is transferred to energy in Alex's **kinetic** energy store to make the pram move.

Q3 'Train A has transferred less energy than Train B' should be ticked.

Q4 (a) Energy from the **chemical** energy store in the battery is transferred **electrically** to the **kinetic** energy store of the car to make it move.

(b) Car C. E.g. this car travelled the smallest distance. As all three cars had the same amount of energy to transfer, it's likely that car C needed a larger force to move C than A or B.

(c) Any two from: e.g. the ground that the cars were driven over / the speed the cars were driven at / the direction the cars were driven in.

Pages 14-15 — Helpful Heating Questions

Quick Fire Questions

Q1 Thermal equilibrium
Q2 Radiation
Q3 An insulator

Practice Questions

Q1

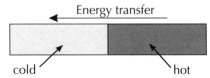

Q2 (a) Conduction
(b)(i) When the end of the wire is heated, its particles start to **vibrate** (shake) more. The particles have got more **energy** than before they were heated.
(ii) The particles pass on energy when they **bump** into other particles that aren't vibrating as much.
(iii) Particles in the hot end of the wire gradually **transfer** energy to particles in the cool end. The cool end gains energy so it **heats up**.

Q3 (a) 'Put the same amount of water in each cup' should be ticked.
(b)(i) Cup B
(ii) E.g. cardboard / polystyrene / plastic
Any insulating material will do here.

Pages 17-18 — Cosy Conservation Questions

Quick Fire Questions

Q1 Energy can never be created nor destroyed — it's only ever transferred from one store to another.
Energy is only useful when it's transferred from one store to another.

Q2 The rest of the energy is wasted (e.g. to thermal energy stores).

Practice Questions

Q1 (a) The energy that she thinks has disappeared has actually been transferred to less **useful** stores.

(b) In the mixer, energy is transferred from the battery's **chemical** energy store to the mixer's **kinetic** energy store.

Q2 'Energy is only useful when it's transferred from one store to another' and 'Useful devices transfer energy from one store to another' should be ticked.

Answers

Q3 (a)(i) Useful energy = energy input – wasted energy
1000 – 750 = **250 J**
(ii) Energy input = useful energy + wasted energy
800 + 3200 = **4000 J**
(b)(i) Kinetic energy store
(ii) E.g. thermal energy store

Page 20 — Fantastic Fuel and Elegant Energy Questions

Quick Fire Questions
Q1 Burn the fuels.
Q2 The Sun

Practice Questions
Q1 Heats atmosphere.
Q2 Light from the Sun hits solar **cells**. This generates **electricity**.
Q3 (a) Photosynthesis
(b)(i) The remains of plants and animals that died millions of years ago.
(ii) Any two from: e.g. coal / oil / natural gas.

Pages 22-23 — Joyful Generating Energy Questions

Quick Fire Questions
Q1 By burning fossil fuels.
Q2 Any two from: e.g. wind / plants (biomass) / waves / solar.

Practice Questions
Q1 The sentences should read:
Renewable energy resources will not run out while the Sun keeps shining.
Non-renewable energy resources will eventually run out.
Q2 (a) Boiler — Burns oil to heat water.
(b) Turbine — Hot gas (e.g. steam) passes through it, causing it to turn.
(c) Generator — Transfers energy away from kinetic energy stores electrically.
Q3 (a)(i) Fossil fuels are a **non-renewable** energy resource.
(ii) Fossil fuels take **millions** of years to form, but only minutes to burn.
(iii) Eventually, we'll **run out** of fossil fuels.
(b) E.g. using less electricity / driving less / using more renewable energy resources.
There are loads of possible answers to this question — any two sensible answers are fine.
Q4 (a) Wind
(b) Waves
(c) Biomass / plants
(d) Solar
Q5 Energy in the kinetic energy stores of the wind turns the turbines. This energy is transferred to the kinetic energy stores of the turbines, then transferred away electrically.

Pages 25-26 — Comfortable Cost of Electricity Questions

Quick Fire Questions
Q1 energy transferred (J) = power (W) × time (seconds)
or energy transferred (kWh) = power (kW) × time (hours)
Q2 The amount of energy transferred, in kilowatt-hours (kWh)
Q3 Cost = energy transferred (kWh) × price per kWh

Practice Questions
Q1 (a) The **energy** used by an appliance in kWh depends on its **power** in kilowatts and the **time** in hours that it is on for.
(b) One kilowatt-hour is the amount of energy used by an appliance with a power of one **kilowatt** used for a time of one **hour**.
Q2 (a) Energy transferred (kWh) = power (kW) × time (hours)
power = 2 kW, time = 1.5 hours
energy transferred = 2 × 1.5 = **3 kWh**
(b) Energy transferred (J) = power (W) × time (seconds)
power = 200 W, time = 150 seconds
Energy transferred = 200 × 150 = **30 000 J**
Q3 17935 – 17920 = **15 kWh**
To find how much energy Alice used, you need to subtract the second meter reading from the first one.
Q4 Cost = energy transferred (kWh) × price per kWh
energy transferred = 20 kWh
price = 15p per kWh
20 × 15 = 300p = **£3.00**
Q5 Cost = energy transferred (kWh) × price per kWh
energy transferred = 61 + 59 + 54 + 60
= 234 kWh
price = 16p per kWh
Cost = 234 × 16 = 3744p = **£37.44**

Page 28 — Plucky Power Ratings and Energy Questions

Quick Fire Questions
Q1 The 2 kW heater.
Q2 The 800 kJ block of butter.

Practice Questions
Q1 Runners Salty Shack Share Bag
Q2 'A measure of how fast the appliance transfers energy' should be ticked.
Q3 Your **body** gets all the energy it needs from the food you eat. Energy in foods is measured in **kilojoules**. You can compare the amount of energy found in different foods by looking at their **labels**.
Q4 No — Kettle 2 has a higher power rating, so it must transfer more energy in a given time than kettle 1.
The question doesn't tell you the size of either of the kettles, so kettle 2 might take longer to boil because it holds more water.

Pages 30-31 — Fantastic Physical Changes Questions

Quick Fire Questions
Q1 Solid, liquid, gas

Answers

Q2 In a physical change there is no chemical reaction and no new substances are made.

Q3 Sublimation

Q4 Gas

Practice Questions

Q1 Evaporating — a liquid changes into a gas
Melting — a solid changes into a liquid
Condensation — a gas changes into a liquid
Dissolving — a solid mixes with a liquid to form a solution

Q2 E.g.

Gas　　Liquid　　Solid

Q3 (a) 108 g
Remember that the mass doesn't change when a physical change occurs.
(b) The liquid water would freeze and turn into ice / a solid.
(c) 108 g

Q4 (a)

	Solid	Liquid	Gas
Density	dense	fairly dense	not dense
How close together are the particles?	tightly packed	fairly close	far apart

(b)(i) E.g. ice / water
(ii) Liquid water has a higher density than solid ice.

Pages 33-34 — Peachy Particle Movement Questions

Quick Fire Questions

Q1 Diffusion is when a substance moves from an area of high concentration to an area of low concentration.

Q2 An increase in temperature causes particles to move around more.

Practice Questions

Q1 (a) Brownian motion is the **random** movement of any particle that is **suspended** (floating) in a liquid or **gas**.
(b) It is the result of **collisions** between particles.

Q2 (a) 'Higher concentration' should be ticked.
(b)(i) Diffusion
(ii) The concentration of deodorant particles will be the same everywhere / the deodorant particles will be evenly spread out.

Q3 (a) E.g. the warm water heats the oil up, so it expands. This pushes it up into the thin tube.
(b) The oil would move back down the thin tube.

Q3 E.g.

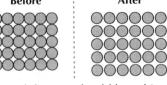

Before　　　　After

The second diagram should have bigger gaps between the particles. But it should have an ordered structure, because it's still a solid.

Section 2 — Forces and Motion

Pages 36-37 — Spiffing Speed Questions

Quick Fire Questions

Q1 Speed is a measure of how far you travel in a set amount of time.

Q2 E.g. metres per second (m/s), miles per hour (mph) and kilometres per hour (km/h).

Q3 The speed at which the object is moving.

Practice Questions

Q1 Speed = **distance ÷ time**

Q2 speed = distance ÷ time
distance = 48 m, time = 120 s
48 ÷ 120 = **0.4 m/s**

Q3 speed = distance ÷ time
distance = 80 miles, time = 2 hours
80 ÷ 2 = **40 mph**

Q4 (a) Between 1 and 2 minutes, the vacuum cleaner is **moving at a steady speed**.
(b) A curve that gets steeper means that the vacuum cleaner is speeding up.
A curve that gets flatter means that the vacuum cleaner is slowing down.
A flat line means that the vacuum cleaner is not moving.
(c) Towards its charger / back towards its start point.

Q5 (a) E.g. the part of the hill they run up / the slope of the hill.
(b) E.g. use a stopwatch / ask a third person to time them both.

Pages 39-40 — Fabulous Forces Questions

Quick Fire Questions

Q1 Forces are pushes or pulls.

Q2 E.g. speed up or start moving, slow down or stop moving, change direction, turn, change shape.

Practice Questions

Q1 (a) A newton meter (or force meter)
(b) Newtons/N

Q2 (a) Non-contact forces.
(b)(i) The two magnets do not need to touch.
(ii) The tractor and the bale of hay do need to touch.
(c)(i) static electricity
(ii) magnetism
(iii) gravity

Q3 (a) speed up
(b) slow down
(c) change direction
(d) change shape

Page 42 — Rocking Resistance Questions

Quick Fire Questions

Q1 Friction always acts in the **opposite** direction to movement.

Q2 Water resistance

Q3 The sheep slows down because when it opens its parachute, the air resistance increases a lot. *The air resistance increases because there is a much larger area trying to cut through the air.*

Practice Questions

Q1 Friction is a force that acts **against** movement. It must be overcome to make any object start moving or **accelerate**. **Air** and water resistance are types of friction.

Q2 (a)(i) When the skydiver first steps out of the plane and begins to fall, air resistance is zero. *There's no air resistance because the skydiver isn't moving yet.*

    (ii) 'It increases' should be ticked.

  (b)

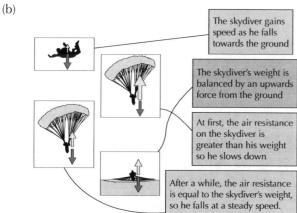

The skydiver gains speed as he falls towards the ground

The skydiver's weight is balanced by an upwards force from the ground

At first, the air resistance on the skydiver is greater than his weight so he slows down

After a while, the air resistance is equal to the skydiver's weight, so he falls at a steady speed.

Pages 44-45 — Fashionable Force Diagram Questions

Quick Fire Questions

Q1

force from table
20 N

20 N
weight of book

Q2 The object will stay still / nothing.

Q3 The object will change its speed or direction.

Practice Questions

Q1 (a) C

  (b) B

Q2 0.5 N

The mug is not moving so the forces must be balanced. The weight of the mug must equal the force from the table.

Q3 (a)

4000 N   4000 N   8000 N

The car is travelling at a steady speed, so the driving force must be equal and opposite to the backwards force.

(b)

4000 N

500 N

Q4 (a) 100 + 6000 − 5500 = **600 N**
Add the forwards forces together then subtract the backwards force.

  (b) Yes, because the forces on it are not balanced / the forwards force is greater than the backwards force (it's accelerating).

Pages 47-48 — Majestic Moments Questions

Quick Fire Questions

Q1 A pivot is a point around which rotation happens.

Q2 Moment = force × distance

Q3 Clockwise and anticlockwise.

Q4 They are equal.

Practice Questions

Q1 (a) Moment

  (b) Nm / newton metres

Q2 moment = force × distance
force = 200 N, distance = 0.75 m
200 × 0.75 = **150 Nm**

Q3 (a)(i) moment = force × distance
force = 500 N, distance = 1 m
500 × 1 = **500 Nm**

    (ii) moment = force × distance
force = 400 N, distance = 1.25 m
400 × 1.25 = **500 Nm**

  (b) The moments are balanced.

Q4 The sliding weight must create a moment of 4 Nm to balance the rice. It has a weight of 4 N.
moment = force × distance
4 Nm = 4 N × distance
distance = 4 Nm ÷ 4 N = **1 m**
If you started off by rearranging the moment formula instead, that's fine too.

Page 50 — Endearing Elasticity Questions

Quick Fire Questions

Q1 They usually spring back to their original shape after the force has been removed.

Q2 Balanced

Practice Questions

Q1 (a) The weight being hung from the spring.

  (b)

```
Weight (N)
1.0 |                              ×
0.8 |                      ×
0.6 |               ×
0.4 |         ×
0.2 |    ×
0.0 ×_____
   0.0 0.5 1.0 1.5 2.0 2.5 3.0 3.5 4.0 4.5 5.0
              Extension (cm)
```

  (c) 2.0 cm

Answers

Pages 52-53 — Peerless Pressure Questions

Quick Fire Questions

Q1   High heels have a smaller area than snow shoes, so they cause a higher pressure on the snow.

Q2   Atmospheric pressure is higher at sea level because there is more atmosphere pressing down on you (so the pressure due to the weight of the atmosphere increases).

Practice Questions

Q1   If the upthrust is smaller than an object's weight the object will sink.
If the upthrust is the greater than an object's weight the object will rise up.

Q2

	True	False
At sea level, the atmosphere doesn't weigh anything.		✓
Atmospheric pressure decreases with height.	✓	
Atmospheric pressure is highest at the top of mountains.		✓
Atmospheric pressure is lower on mountains than at sea level.	✓	
Atmospheric pressure stays the same wherever you are.		✓

Q3 (a) pressure = force ÷ area
      (b) 1. Pascals (Pa)
           2. Newtons per metre squared (N/m^2)
      (c) Pressure = force ÷ area
           force = 450 N, area = 0.02 m^2
           450 ÷ 0.02 = **22 500 Pa** (or N/m^2)

Q4   E.g. pressure is force divided by area. Wide straps have a larger area and will exert a lower pressure for the same force than narrow straps. So a rucksack with wide straps will put less pressure on your shoulders / will not dig into your shoulders so much.

Section 3 — Waves

Pages 55-56 — Wonderful Water Wave Questions

Quick Fire Questions

Q1   Transverse

Q2   The crests join together to make a bigger crest.

Q3   E.g. a sea wall.
You could write pretty much any solid surface for your answer here.

Practice Questions

Q1 (a) Water waves are undulations with **up and down** movements.
      (b) These undulations are **at right angles to** the direction the wave is travelling in.
      (c) Water waves transfer energy in the direction **they're travelling in**.

Q2

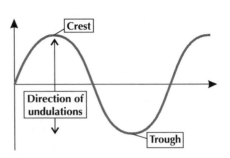

Q3 (a)

      (b)

For this one, the crest height needs to be bigger than the height of the crests in the first two waves.

      (c)

For this one, the trough depth needs to be bigger than the depth of the troughs in the first two waves.

      (d)

Pages 58-59 — Lovely Light Questions

Quick Fire Questions

Q1   True

Q2   E.g. they are both transverse waves / they both transfer energy / they can both be reflected.

Q3   300 000 000 m/s

Practice Questions

Q1   'a star', 'a laser' and 'a candle' should be ticked.

Q2   E.g. water waves need particles to travel through, light waves do not.

Q3   Light travels fastest when it's travelling through **a vacuum**.
In a vacuum, the speed of light is always **the same**. When light travels through **particles** it slows down.

Q4 (a) E.g.

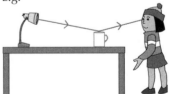

      (b) Light is produced by the lamp. It travels to the mug where some of it is reflected into Charmaine's eyes.
      (c) Light waves always travel in straight lines — they cannot travel around corners. So none of the light that is reflected off the mug will reach Dan's eyes.

Answers

Pages 61-62 — Remarkable Reflection Questions

Quick Fire Questions
Q1 A smooth, shiny surface.
Q2 The normal
Q3 45°
The angle of reflection is the same as the angle of incidence.

Practice Questions
Q1 (a) Mirrors have **smooth** surfaces.
(b) When light reflects off a mirror, it's all reflected off at **the same angle**.
(c) This is called **specular** reflection.
(d) Paper has a **rough** surface.
(e) When light reflects off paper, it's all reflected off at **different angles**.
(f) This is called **diffuse** scattering.

Q2 (a) and (b)

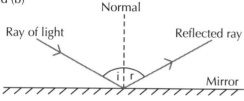

(c) The law of reflection says that the angle of incidence is the same as the angle of reflection. / angle of incidence = angle of reflection.

Q3 (a)

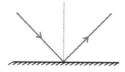

(b)

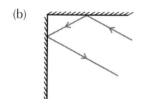

(c)

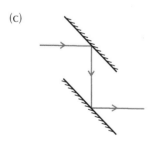

Pages 64-65 — Radical Refraction Questions

Quick Fire Questions
Q1 No
Q2 It refracts (bends).
Q3 No

Practice Questions
Q1 (a) **Refraction** is when light bends while passing from one transparent material to another.
(b) When light goes from a less dense medium to a more dense medium, it bends **towards** the normal.

(c) When light goes from a more dense medium to a less dense medium, it bends **away from** the normal.

Q2 (a) E.g. Keep the light source the same. / Keep the angle of incidence the same.
(b)(i) When light passes from air to water it bends **towards** the normal. This shows that water is **more** dense than air.
(ii) When light passes from air to glass it bends **towards** the normal. This shows that glass is **more** dense than air.

Q3 (a)

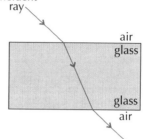

(b)

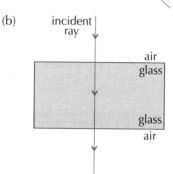

Pages 67-68 — Legendary Lenses and Cameras Questions

Quick Fire Questions
Q1 E.g. a lens.
Q2 Outwards
Q3 A light absorber.

Practice Questions
Q1 (a)

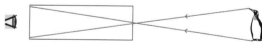

(b)

Q2 (a) The human eye contains a **convex** lens.
(b) This type of lens causes rays of light to move **together**.
(c) Images are formed on the **retina**, where there are light-sensitive cells.

Answers

Q3 (a) E.g.

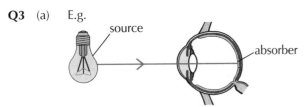

You should have labelled the light bulb as the source and the retina of the eye as the absorber.

 (b) Energy

 (c)(i) The retina

 (ii) The brain

Page 70 — Lively Light and Colour Questions

Quick Fire Questions

Q1 The white light gets split up into a spectrum/full rainbow of colours.

Q2 The number of light waves that pass a point per second.

Practice Questions

Q1 red, orange, yellow, green, blue, indigo, violet

Q2 (a)(i) a spectrum

 (ii) dispersal

 (b)(i) Red

 (ii) Violet

 (c) Violet

Pages 72-73 — Astounding Absorption and Reflection Questions

Quick Fire Questions

Q1 Violet

Q2 Yes

Q3 White

Q4 Black

Practice Questions

Q1 The true statements are (a) and (f).

Q2 (a) If white light shines on a red filter, **red** light is let through.

 (b) If white light shines on a yellow surface, **yellow** light is reflected.

 (c) If blue light shines on a yellow filter, **no** light is let through.

 (d) If red light shines on a green surface, **no** light is reflected.

Q3 (a)

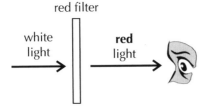

 (b)

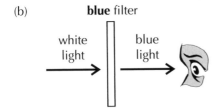

(c)

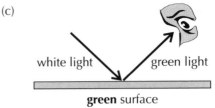

(d)

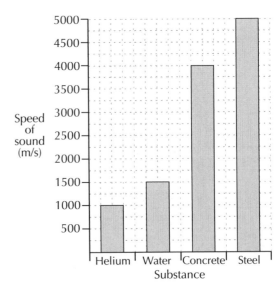

Q4 (a) Under a blue light, the blue sections of the car appear **blue**, the white sections appear **blue** and the black sections appear **black**.

 (b)(i) The white sections would look red because white objects reflect red light/all colours of light.

 (ii) The blue sections would look black because blue objects absorb/do not reflect red light.

 (iii) The black sections would look black because black objects absorb all colours of light/do not reflect any colours of light.

Pages 75-76 — Sensational Sound Questions

Quick Fire Questions

Q1 Yes

Q2 It can be reflected or absorbed.

Q3 Solids

Practice Questions

Q1 (a) Sound waves are **longitudinal** waves.

 (b) Sound waves have vibrations **in the same direction as** the direction of the wave.

Q2 (a)(i) The sound waves were **reflected by** the walls of the cave.

 (ii) An echo.

 (b) The right answer is: The second sound has further to travel than the first sound.

Q3

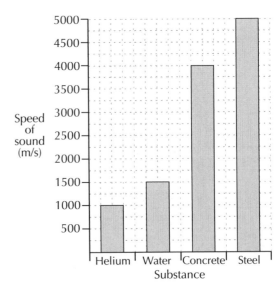

Q4 (a) Sound **waves** can't travel without **particles** — they need a **medium** like air to travel through. This means that sound can't travel in **space** because it's mostly a **vacuum** (which is an area where there are **no** particles).

(b) When the two helmets are touching, sound waves **can** travel through the particles in the helmets. This means that Joel **can** hear Zach speaking to him.

Page 78 — Hysterical Hearing Questions

Quick Fire Questions
Q1 The ear drum.
Q2 High
Q3 Hertz (Hz)
Q4 Auditory range is the range of frequencies that you can hear.

Practice Questions
Q1 (a) Sheep and dolphin
(b) Elephant
Q2 (a) The frequency of a sound is the number of **waves/vibrations** per **second**.
(b) The higher the frequency of a sound, the more high-pitched it will be. / The lower the frequency of a sound, the more low-pitched it will be.
Q3 1. object vibrates
2. air vibrates
3. eardrum vibrates
4. ear bones vibrate
5. hairs vibrate in cochlea and produce electrical signals
6. nerve carries electrical signals to brain

Pages 80-81 — Exciting Energy and Waves Questions

Quick Fire Questions
Q1 Sound waves transfer information through vibrations between particles.
Q2 The diaphragm
Q3 Any sound with a frequency higher than 20 000 Hz. / High frequency sound waves that humans can't hear.

Practice Questions
Q1 (a) All waves transfer energy and **information**.
(b) Microphones detect this information through vibrations in the **diaphragm**.
(c) After the microphone has detected the information, it converts it to **electrical** signals.
(d) Loud speakers can convert these signals back into **sound** waves.
Q2 1. a wire carries an electrical signal into the loudspeaker
2. electrical signals make the diaphragm vibrate
3. the diaphragm makes the air vibrate to produce sound
Q3 (a) The vibrations from the ultrasound waves remove dirt from the false teeth.
(b) E.g. jewellery
(c)(i) Ultrasound waves can travel through the body, so they can get to hard to reach places inside it.

(ii) E.g. the patient was treated using traditional physiotherapy as well — it might have been this that cured them (or they might even have just got better on their own), so we don't know for certain that the ultrasound therapy worked.

Section 4 — Electricity and Magnetism

Pages 83-84 — Splendid Circuit Questions

Quick Fire Questions
Q1 No
Q2 resistance = potential difference ÷ current

Practice Questions
Q1 (a) In an electrical circuit the **cell** (or **battery**) is like a pump because **it pushes the charge around the circuit**.
(b) The current would stop flowing.
Q2 (a)(i) Resistance **slows down** the flow of current.
(ii) Resistance is measured in **ohms**.
(iii) Conductors have a **low** resistance.
(b)(i) Insulators
(ii) Plastic, paper and limestone should be circled.
Q3 (a) The current flowing through the materials.
(b)(i) B
(ii) E.g. metal / any named metal / graphite.
Q4 Resistance = potential difference ÷ current
= 3 V ÷ 2 A = **1.5 Ω**

Page 86 — Curious Current and Victorious Voltmeter Questions

Quick Fire Questions
Q1 1.51 A
Q2 The maximum potential difference that you can safely put across it.

Practice Questions
Q1 A voltmeter is used to measure the potential difference across a component.
Potential difference is measured in volts (or V for short).
Current is measured in amperes (or amps, A for short).
An ammeter is used to measure the current in a circuit.
Q2 (a)(i) ⊣⊢

(ii) —Ⓥ—

(b)(i) A bulb
(ii) An ammeter
(c) An open switch.
Q3

Answers

Page 88 — Super Series and Perfect Parallel Circuit Questions

Quick Fire Questions

Q1 False.
In a series circuit the current stays the same all the way around the circuit.

Q2 In a series circuit the current has no choice of route. There is only one way it can go around the circuit. In a parallel circuit, there's more than one route that the current could take.

Practice Questions

Q1

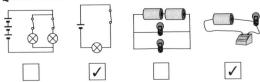

	✓		✓

Q2 (a) A series circuit.
(b) 6.5 A

Q3 (a) A_3
(b)(i) A_1
(ii) Add up the readings on A_2, A_3 and A_4.

Page 90 — Stupendous Static Electricity Questions

Quick Fire Questions

Q1 E.g. rub the rod with a cloth.
Q2 Negative
Q3 An object that loses electrons becomes positively charged.
Q4 True

Practice Questions

Q1

		attract	repel	no effect
⊕ positive	⊕ positive		✓	
⊕ positive	⊖ negative	✓		
⊖ negative	⊖ negative		✓	
○ no charge	○ no charge			✓

Q2 (a) Charged objects have **an electric** field around them.
(b) This is an area where **charged** objects will feel a force acting on them.

Q3 (a) The balloon is negatively charged.
(b) The cloth is positively charged.
(c) Electrons were scraped off the cloth and left on the balloon by the rubbing action.

Pages 92-93 — Magnificent Magnet Questions

Quick Fire Questions

Q1 The North pole and the South pole.
Q2 The South pole.
Q3 To the Earth's magnetic North pole.

Practice Questions

Q1 (a)(i) Like poles **repel** each other.
(ii) Opposite poles **attract** each other.

(b)(i)

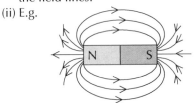

S	N		N	S	or	N	S		S	N

(ii)

S	N		S	N	or	N	S		N	S

Q2 (a)(i) A magnetic field is a region around a magnet where other magnets and magnetic materials experience a **force**.
(ii) This means that the magnet **attracts** or repels them.
(iii) You can use a **compass** to plot the magnetic field lines around a magnet.
(iv) These lines always point from the magnet's **North** pole to its **South** pole.
(b)(i) It will point from North to South along the field lines.
(ii) E.g.

![Magnetic field lines around a bar magnet labelled N and S]

Q3 Sam's **compass** was affected by the magnetic field of the **magnet** in his wallet. This meant that it was not pointing towards the magnetic North **pole** of the **Earth**. So Sam walked in the wrong **direction** and got lost.

Pages 95-96 — Exciting Electromagnet Questions

Quick Fire Questions

Q1 An electric current flowing through it.
Q2 Increasing the number of turns on the coil increases the strength of the electromagnet.
Q3 E.g. an electric motor.

Practice Questions

Q1 (a)(i) Coil of wire
(ii) (Soft) iron core
(iii) Power supply / cell / battery
(b) No pins.
Electromagnets only work when there's current flowing through the wire coil. If there's no power, there's no current and no magnetic force.

Q2 (a) E.g. don't get water anywhere near any electrical devices / don't touch any bare or frayed electrical wires / don't put too much potential difference across components that can't handle it / make sure to turn electrical devices off when not using them / check if a component is hot before touching by placing a hand near it.

(b)

Current (A)	Number of paperclips picked up			
	Try 1	Try 2	Try 3	Average
0.0	0	0	0	**0**
1.0	14	16	15	**15**
2.0	31	27	32	**30**
3.0	47	47	44	**46**

picks up about **15** extra paperclips.

(d) 22 paperclips

The number of paperclips increases by about 15 for each 1 A increase in current. So if you increase the current by 0.5 A, the number of paperclips picked up should go up by about half of that.

(e)

Variable	Independent	Dependent	Control
Current	✓		
Number of paperclips picked up		✓	
Size and mass of paperclips			✓
The core of the electromagnet			✓

(f) E.g. Jason could change the number of turns in the wire coil.

Section 5 — The Earth and Beyond

Pages 98-99 — Great Gravity Questions

Quick Fire Questions
Q1 The force of attraction between two objects is due to **gravity**.
Q2 10 N/kg
Q3 False
Weight is a force caused by the pull of gravity. Mass is not a force.

Practice Questions
Q1 (a) Your weight is a force caused by the pull of **gravity**.
(b) This force pulls you **towards** the Earth.
(c) If you went to a planet with a different gravitational field strength to Earth, your **weight** would be different, but your **mass** would stay the same.
Q2 (a) 'The Earth is also attracted to the Moon.' should be ticked.
(b) '... stronger than the force of gravity between the Earth and the Moon.' should be ticked.
Q3 (a) An astronaut walking on the Moon has less **weight** than they would do on Earth.
(b) This is because force of gravity is **weaker** on the Moon than on Earth.
Q4 (a) weight = mass × gravitational field strength
(b)(i) weight = mass × gravitational field strength = 70 kg × 10 N/kg = **700 N**
(ii) weight = mass × gravitational field strength = 70 kg × 3.7 N/kg = **259 N**
(iii) weight = mass × gravitational field strength = 70 kg × 25 N/kg = **1750 N**

Pages 101-102 — Sublime Sun and Star Questions

Quick Fire Questions

Q1 The Sun
Q2 Any two from: Mercury / Venus / Earth / Mars / Jupiter / Saturn / Uranus / Neptune.
Q3 A light year is a unit of distance.

Practice Questions
Q1 (a) The Sun
(b)(i) A galaxy is a large group of stars.
(ii) 'The Milky Way' should be ticked.
Q2

Object	Description	Example
Planet	A large object that **orbits** a **star**	E.g **Earth**
Star	A huge ball of hot **gas** that gives out heat and **light**.	E.g. **the Sun**

There are loads of possible planets and stars you could have here.

Q3 (a) The distance that light travels in one year.
(b) 9.5 trillion km
(c) Betelgeuse
(d)(i) 640 years
(ii) 2000 − 640 years = **1360**
Light from distant stars has to travel a really long way to reach the Earth, so takes a really long time. When you look at Betelgeuse from the Earth, what you're actually seeing is light that left the star 640 years ago.

Pages 104-105 — Dapper Day, Nifty Night and Super Season Questions

Quick Fire Questions
Q1 24 hours (1 day)
Q2 1 year (accept 365¼ days)
Q3 The UK is in the northern hemisphere. During winter, the northern hemisphere is tilted away from the Sun, so the UK gets fewer hours of sunlight.

Practice Questions
Q1 (a) 'It is midday.' should be ticked.
(b) 'It is late at night.' should be ticked.
Q2

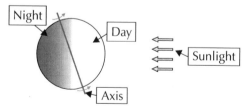

Q3 (a) The time it takes the Earth to orbit once around the Sun.
(b) Winter
(c)(i) B
(ii) A
(d) The northern hemisphere is **warmer** in summer because it is tilted **towards** the Sun.

ISBN 978 1 78294 109 5

9 781782 941095

SFQA32   £2.00
(Retail Price)

www.cgpbooks.co.uk